PREFACE

TO sing songs of joy and gladness on the Holy Night of the Saviour's birth, to welcome the Happy Morning of the Risen Lord with carols of praise and thanksgiving is a practice which has lasted throughout centuries and grows more common year by year. Creeds, theologies, sects and denominations are forgotten as all nations of Christendom join in the universal chorus.

MANY of these manifestations of simple unaffected gladness are distinctively national and all are truly popular in the best sense of the word. I have attempted to bring together in this volume a group of carols which shall be a genuinely international expression of the Christmas spirit.

THE nations whose Christmas songs have been fairly well known in the past are represented in each case by a number of old favorites, but I have also selected in such cases a few characteristic carols which were not so well known, but which merit a more frequent use. In addition I have included specimens of the Christmas melodies of peoples whose music has only recently been made current in the community of nations, and which are here offered in an easily accessible form in singable translations for the first time.

THE singing of carols, as of all folk music, is essentially a unison performance. This is the form used in the Sunday-school, the community chorus and the family circle. My collection will, I hope, be found adaptable to all these uses. Nevertheless I have arranged most of the numbers in simple and appropriate four-part harmony, so that they may be used by trained choirs and choruses which aim at a higher artistic production.

IN a few cases, however, among the Italian, Spanish and Portuguese pieces, where the tune was so essentially and exclusively melodic, I have chosen the form of a unison melody, or at most the simplest and most popular kind of two-part singing, adding an instrumental accompaniment for organ or piano which might represent the unadorned accompaniment which folk-singers would produce on their native instruments.

Eduardo Marzo

Fifty Christmas Carols of All Nations

CONTENTS

ENGLISH

	Page
God rest you merry, gentlemen	2
Golden carol	4
The first Nowell	5
I saw three ships	6
Good King Wenceslas	7
The holly and the ivy	8
We three Kings of Orient are	10
What Child is this?	12
The seven joys of Mary	14
O little town of Bethlehem	16
The cherry tree carol	17
The Babe of Bethlehem	18

GERMAN

Silent Night (Stille Nacht)	20
As each happy Christmas (Alle Jahre wieder)	21
O Christmas tree (O Tannenbaum)	22
Away in a manger (Luther's carol)	23
O come, little children (Ihr Kinderlein kommet)	24

DUTCH

In Bethlehem, the lowly (In Bethlehem geboren)	26
Sleep my little one (Slaap, mijn kindjelief)	27
Once came an Angel (Daar komt een Engel)	28

BOHEMIAN

Let our gladness know no end	29
Come all ye shepherds	30

ALSATIAN

Oh sleep, sleep on, thou fair child Jesus	31

AUSTRIAN

As lately we watched	32

POLISH

In a manger He is lying (Wzlobia lezy Etoz pobiezy)	33

Fifty Christmas Carols of All Nations—*Continued*   iii

RUSSIAN
	Page
Kolyada (Father Christmas)	34

SWEDISH
O fir tree dark, o fir tree dear	35

DANISH
Christmas brings joy to every heart	36

FRENCH
The Angel and the shepherds (French Flanders)	38
Whence comes this rush of wings (Carol of the birds)	40
Come with us, sweet flowers (Carol of the flowers)	41
Shepherds, shake your drowsy sleep (Chantans! Bargiés, noué, noué)	42
Angels we have heard on high (Bergers, pour qui cette fête?)	44
Here in a stable (Dans cette étable)	46
Close by the Ox and the Ass so gray (Entre le bœuf et l'âne gris)	47
Glad news from Bethlehem (M'es esta dì). Noël provençal	48
Ah, great is our good fortune (Ay, la bono fortuno). Noël provençal	49
The children at the manger (Les enfants à la crecho). Noël de Bousquet	50
The message of Christmas morning (Lei pastorieu). Noël provençal	52

SPANISH
The song of the birds (El cant des ancels)—Catalan	54
Companions, all sing loudly (Khanta zagun guzick ahalik gorena)—Basque	56
Fum, fum, fum—Catalan	57
Wake, o wake, ye shepherds all (El Rabada)—Catalan	58
Come all ye children (Venid niños queridos)—Castilla	59

PORTUGUESE
All that wondrous Christmas night (Noite de Natal)	60
From the Orient they came ariding (Os reis)	61

ITALIAN and LATIN
When Christ was born on earth (I Zampognari)—Neapolitan	62
O thou joyful day (O santissima)—Sicilian	64
Lullu, lully, lu (Qui creavit cœlum, lully, lully, lu)—Latin	65
O come all ye faithful (Adeste fideles)	66

INDEX

		Page
AH, GREAT IS OUR GOOD FORTUNE (Ay, la bono fortuno)	French	49
ALL THAT WONDROUS CHRISTMAS NIGHT (Noite de Natal)	Portuguese	60
ANGEL AND THE SHEPHERDS, THE	French-Flanders	38
ANGELS WE HAVE HEARD ON HIGH (Bergers, pour qui cette fête)	French	44
AS EACH HAPPY CHRISTMAS (Alle Jahre wieder)	German	21
AS LATELY WE WATCHED	Austrian	32
AWAY IN A MANGER (Luther's Carol)	German	23
BABE OF BETHLEHEM, THE	English	18
CHERRY TREE CAROL, THE	English	17
CHILDREN AT THE MANGER, THE (Les enfants a la crecho. Noël de Bousquet)	French	50
CHRISTMAS BRINGS JOY TO EVERY HEART	Danish	36
CLOSE BY THE OX AND THE ASS SO GRAY (Entre le bœuf et l'âne gris)	French	47
COME ALL YE CHILDREN (Venid ninos queridos)—Castilla	Spanish	59
COME ALL YE SHEPHERDS	Bohemian	30
COMPANIONS, ALL SING LOUDLY (Khanta zagun guzick ahalik gorena)—Basque	Spanish	56
COME WITH US, SWEET FLOWERS (Carol of flowers)	French	41
FIRST NOWELL, THE	English	5
FROM THE ORIENT THEY CAME A'RIDING (Os reis)	Portuguese	61
FUM, FUM, FUM—Catalan	Spanish	57
GLAD NEWS FROM BETHLEHEM (M'es esta di) (Noël provençal)	French	48
GOD REST YOU MERRY, GENTLEMEN	English	2
GOLDEN CAROL	English	4
GOOD KING WENCESLAS	English	7
HERE IN A STABLE (Dans cette etable)	French	46
HOLLY AND THE IVY, THE	English	8
IN A MANGER HE IS LYING (Wzlobia lezy ktoz po biezy)	Polish	33
IN BETHLEHEM, THE LOWLY (In Bethlehem geboren)	Dutch	26
I SAW THREE SHIPS	English	6
KOLYADA (Father Christmas)	Russian	34
LET OUR GLADNESS KNOW NO END	Bohemian	29
LULLY, LULLY, LU (Qui creavit cœlum, lully, lully, lu)	Italian and Latin	65
MESSAGE OF CHRISTMAS MORNING (Lei pastorieu) (Noël provençal)	French	52
O CHRISTMAS TREE (O Tannenbaum)	German	22
O COME ALL YE FAITHFUL (Adeste Fideles)	Latin	66
O COME LITTLE CHILDREN (Ihr Kinderlein kommet)	German	24
O FIR TREE DARK, O FIR TREE DEAR	Swedish	35
O LITTLE TOWN OF BETHLEHEM	English	16
ONCE CAME AN ANGEL (Daar komt een Engel)	Dutch	28
O SLEEP, SLEEP ON, THOU FAIR CHILD JESUS	Alsatian	31

INDEX—Continued

		Page
O Thou Joyful Day (O santissima)	*Italian and Latin*	64
Seven Joys of Mary, The	*English*	14
Shepherds, shake your drowsy sleep (Chantons! Bargiés, Noué, Noué)	*French*	42
Silent Night (Stille Nacht)	*German*	20
Sleep My Little One (Slaap mijn kindjelief)	*Dutch*	27
Song of the Birds (El cant des aucels)—Catalan	*Spanish*	54
Wake, O Wake, ye Shepherds all (El Rabada)—Catalan	*Spanish*	58
We Three Kings of the Orient are	*English*	10
What Child is This?	*English*	12
Whence comes this rush of wings (Carol of the birds)	*French*	40
When Christ was born on earth (I Zampoguari)	*Italian*	62

God Rest You Merry, Gentlemen

Traditional
Harmonized by Sir John Stainer

Copyright, MCMXXIII, by The Willis Music Co.
Printed in the U.S.A.

4.

"Fear not then," said the Angel,
  "Let nothing you affright,
This day is born a Saviour
  Of a pure Virgin bright,
To free all those who trust in Him,
  From Satan's power and might."
    O tidings, etc.

5.

The Shepherds at those tidings
  Rejoiced much in mind,
And left their flocks a-feeding,
  In tempest, storm, and wind:
And went to Bethlehem straightway,
  The Son of God to find.
    O tidings, etc.

6.

And when they came to Bethlehem,
  Where our dear Saviour lay,
They found Him in a manger,
  Where oxen feed on hay;
His Mother Mary kneeling down,
  Unto the Lord did pray.
    O tidings, etc.

7.

Now to the Lord sing praises,
  All you within this place,
And with true love and brotherhood
  Each other now embrace;
This holy tide of Christmas
  All other doth deface.
    O tidings, etc.

W. M. Co. 4141

The Golden Carol
of Melchoir, Bathazer and Caspar

Old English

The First Nowell

Words traditional

Harmonized by Sir John Stainer

1. The first Nowell the angel did say Was to certain poor shepherds in fields as they lay; In fields where they lay keeping their sheep On a cold winter's night that was so deep.
2. They looked up and saw a Star Shining in the East, beyond them far, And to the earth it gave great light, And so it continued both day and night.
3. This star drew nigh to the north-west, O'er Bethlehem it took its rest, And there it did both hop and stay Right over the place where Jesus lay.
4. Then enter'd in there wise men three, Full rev'rently upon their knee, And offer'd there in His presence, Their gold and myrrh and frankincense.

Chorus

Nowell, Nowell, Nowell, Nowell, Born is the King of Israel.

W. M. Co. 4141

I Saw Three Ships

Traditional

2.
And what was in those ships all three,
  On Christmas day, on Christmas day?
And what was in those ships all three,
  On Christmas day in the morning?

3.
The Virgin Mary and Christ were there,
  On Christmas day, on Christmas day;
The Virgin Mary and Christ were there,
  On Christmas day in the morning.

4.
Pray, whither sailed those ships all three,
  On Christmas day, on Christmas day;
Pray, whither sailed those ships all three,
  On Christmas day in the morning.

5.
O they sailed into Bethlehem,
  On Christmas day, on Christmas day;
O they sailed into Bethlehem,
  On Christmas day in the morning.

6.
And all the bells on earth shall ring,
  On Christmas day, on Christmas day;
And all the bells on earth shall ring,
  On Christmas day in the morning.

7.
And all the Angels in Heaven shall sing
  On Christmas day, on Christmas day;
And all the Angels in Heaven shall sing
  On Christmas day in the morning.

8.
And all the souls on earth shall sing,
  On Christmas day, on Christmas day;
And all the souls on earth shall sing,
  On Christmas day in the morning.

9.
Then let us all rejoice amain,
  On Christmas day, on Christmas day;
Then let us all rejoice amain,
  On Christmas day in the morning.

Good King Wenceslas

Traditional
Harmonized by Sir John Stainer

1. Good King Wenceslas look'd out On the Feast of Stephen, When the snow lay 'round about, Deep and crisp and even: Brightly shone the moon that night, Though the frost was cruel, When a poor man came in sight, Gath'ring winter fuel.

2. "Hither, page, and stand by me, If thou know'st it telling, Yonder peasant, who is he? Where and what his dwelling?" "Sire, he lives a good league hence, Underneath the mountain; Right against the forest fence, By Saint Agnes' fountain."

3. "Bring me flesh, and bring me wine, Bring me pine-logs hither, Thou and I will see him dine, When we bear them thither." Page and monarch forth they went, Forth they went together; Through the rude winds wild lament, And the bitter weather.

4.
"Sire, the night is darker now,
  And the wind blows stronger;
Fails my heart, I know not how,
  I can go no longer."
"Mark my footsteps, my good page,
  Tread thou in them boldly:
Thou shalt find the winter's rage
  Freeze thy blood less coldly."

5.
In his master's steps he trod,
  Where the snow lay dinted;
Heat was in the very sod
  Which the saint had printed.
Therefore, Christian men, be sure,
  Wealth or rank possessing,
Ye who now will bless the poor,
  Shall yourselves find blessing.

W. M. Co. 4141

The Holly and the Ivy

Words traditional
Old French Melody

1. The hol-ly and the i-vy Now both are full well
2. The hol-ly bears a blos-som, As white as an-y
3. The hol-ly bears a ber-ry, As red as an-y
4. The hol-ly bears a prick-le As sharp as an-y
5. The hol-ly bears a bark, As bit-ter as an-y

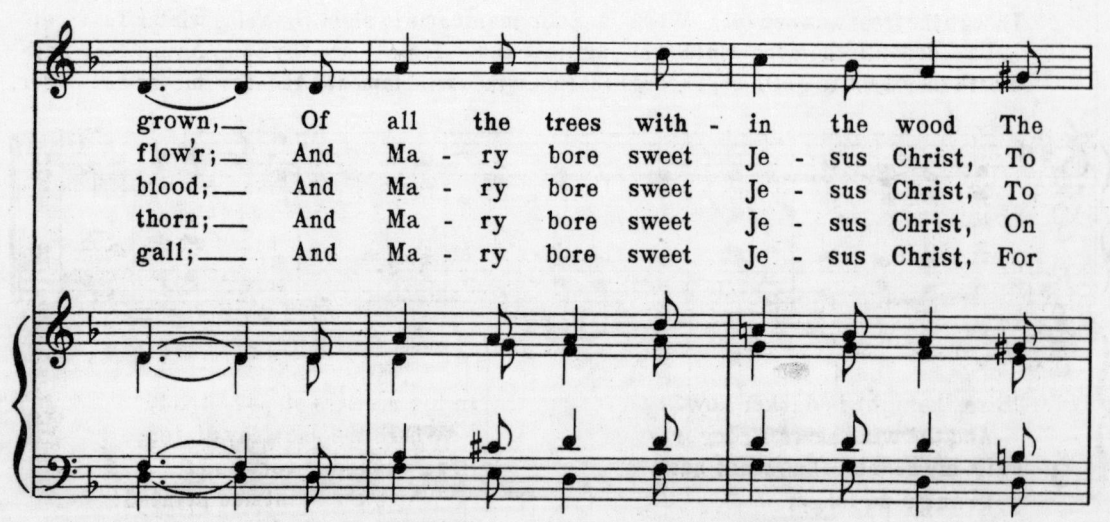

grown, Of all the trees with-in the wood The
flow'r; And Ma-ry bore sweet Je-sus Christ, To
blood; And Ma-ry bore sweet Je-sus Christ, To
thorn; And Ma-ry bore sweet Je-sus Christ, On
gall; And Ma-ry bore sweet Je-sus Christ, For

We Three Kings of Orient Are

J. H. Hopkins

1. We three kings of
Melchoir: 2. Born a King on
Caspar: 3. Frank-in-cense to
Balthazar: 4. Myrrh is mine, its
5. Glo-rious now be-

O - rient are; Bear - ing gifts we tra-verse a - far
Beth-le-hem's plain, Gold I bring, to crown Him a - gain,
of - fer have I, In - cense owns a De - i - ty nigh,
bit - ter per - fume Breathes a life of gath-er-ing gloom,
hold Him a - rise, King and God and sac - ri - fice,

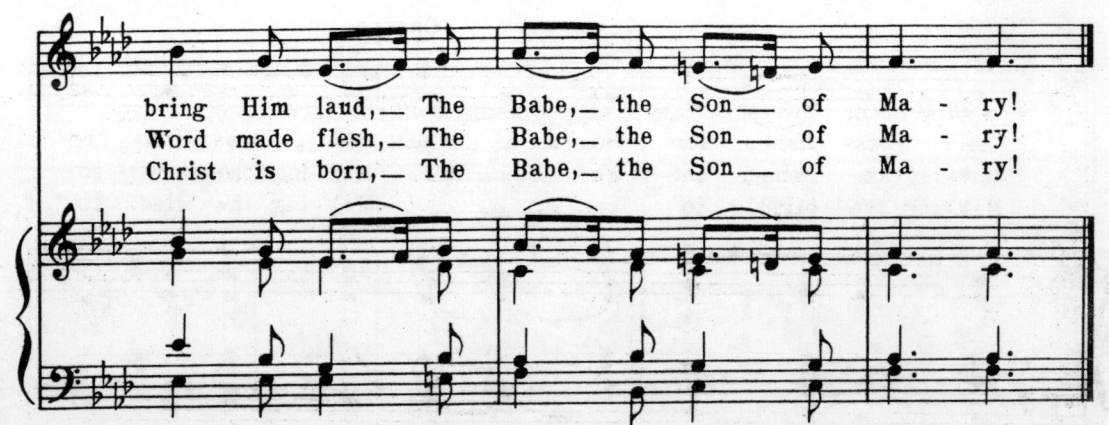

The Seven Joys of Mary

Traditional

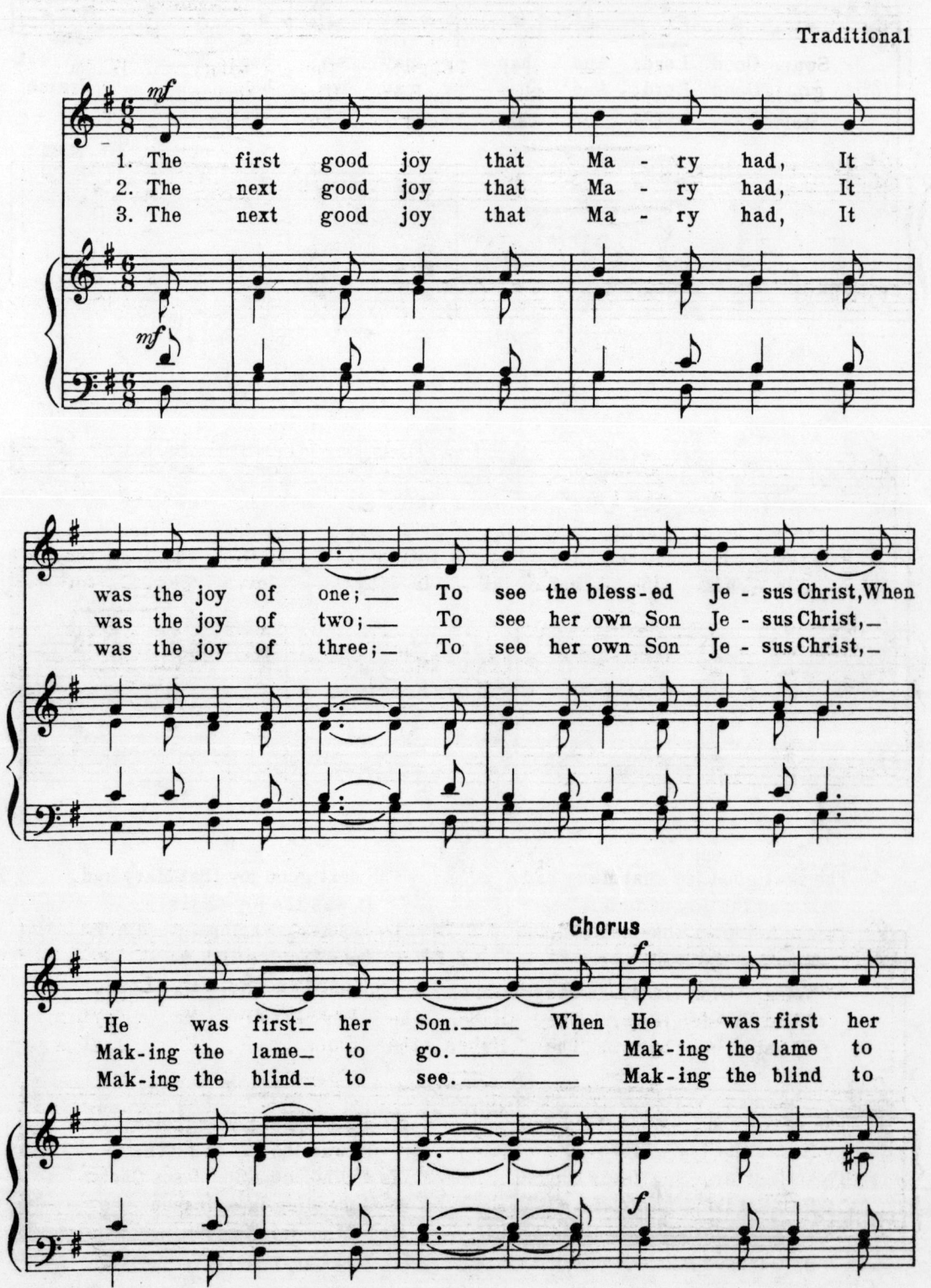

1. The first good joy that Mary had, It was the joy of one; To see the bless-ed Jesus Christ, When He was first her Son. When He was first her
2. The next good joy that Mary had, It was the joy of two; To see her own Son Jesus Christ, Mak-ing the lame to go. Mak-ing the lame to
3. The next good joy that Mary had, It was the joy of three; To see her own Son Jesus Christ, Mak-ing the blind to see. Mak-ing the blind to

4.

The next good joy that Mary had,
 It was the joy of four;
To see her own Son Jesus Christ
 Reading the Bible o'er.
Reading the Bible o'er, Good Lord;
 And happy etc.

5.

The next good joy that Mary had,
 It was the joy of five;
To see her own Son Jesus Christ
 Raising the dead to life.
Raising the dead to life, Good Lord;
 And happy etc.

6.

The next good joy that Mary had,
 It was the joy of six;
To see her own Son Jesus Christ
 Upon the Crucifix.
Upon the Crucifix, Good Lord.
 And happy etc.

7.

The next good joy that Mary had,
 It was the joy of seven;
To see her own Son Jesus Christ
 Ascending into Heaven.
Ascending into Heaven, Good Lord.
 And happy etc.

O Little Town of Bethlehem

P. Brooks, 1868 — L. H. Redner, 1868

The Cherry Tree Carol

Traditional

1. Joseph was an old man, An old man was he; He married sweet Mary, The Queen of Galilee.

2. As they went a-walking In the garden so gay, Maid Mary spied cherries, Hanging over yon tree.

3.
Mary said to Joseph,
   With her sweet lips so mild,
'Pluck those cherries, Joseph,
   For to give to my Child".

4.
"O then", replied Joseph,
   With words so unkind,
"I will pluck no cherries
   For to give to thy Child".

5.
Mary said to cherry-tree
   "Bow down to my knee,
That I may pluck cherries
   By one, two, and three".

6.
The uppermost sprig then
   Bowed down to her knee:
"Thus you may see, Joseph,
   These cherries are for me".

7.
"O eat your cherries, Mary,
   O eat your cherries now,
O eat your cherries, Mary,
   That grow upon the bough".

8.
As Joseph was a-walking
   He heard Angels sing,
"This night there shall be born
   Our Heavenly King.

9.
"He neither shall be born
   In house nor in hall,
Nor in the place of Paradise,
   But in an ox stall.

10.
"He shall not be clothed
   In purple nor pall;
But all in fair linen,
   As wear babies all.

11.
"He shall not be rocked,
   In silver nor gold,
But in a wooden cradle
   That rocks on the mould.

12.
"He neither shall be christened
   In milk nor in wine,
But in pure spring-well water
   Fresh sprung from Bethine".

13.
Mary took her Baby,
   She dressed Him so sweet,
She laid Him in a manger
   All there for to sleep.

14.
As she stood over Him
   She heard Angels sing,
"Oh! bless our dear Saviour,
   Our heavenly King".

* This introductory chord will be necessary for verses 4, 6, 7, 8, 9 and 12

The Babe of Bethlehem

Traditional

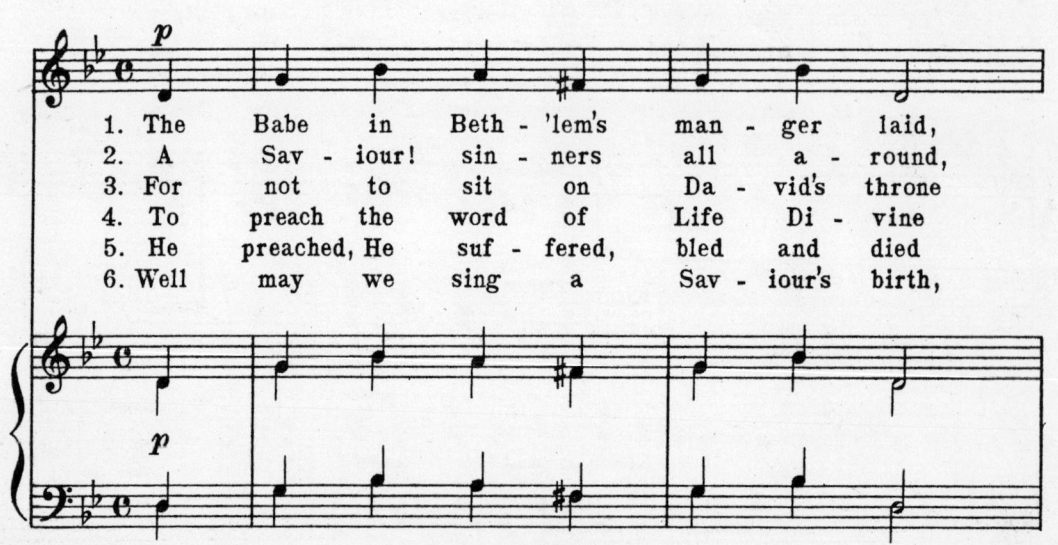

1. The Babe in Beth-'lem's manger laid,
2. A Saviour! sinners all a-round,
3. For not to sit on David's throne
4. To preach the word of Life Divine
5. He preached, He suffered, bled and died
6. Well may we sing a Saviour's birth,

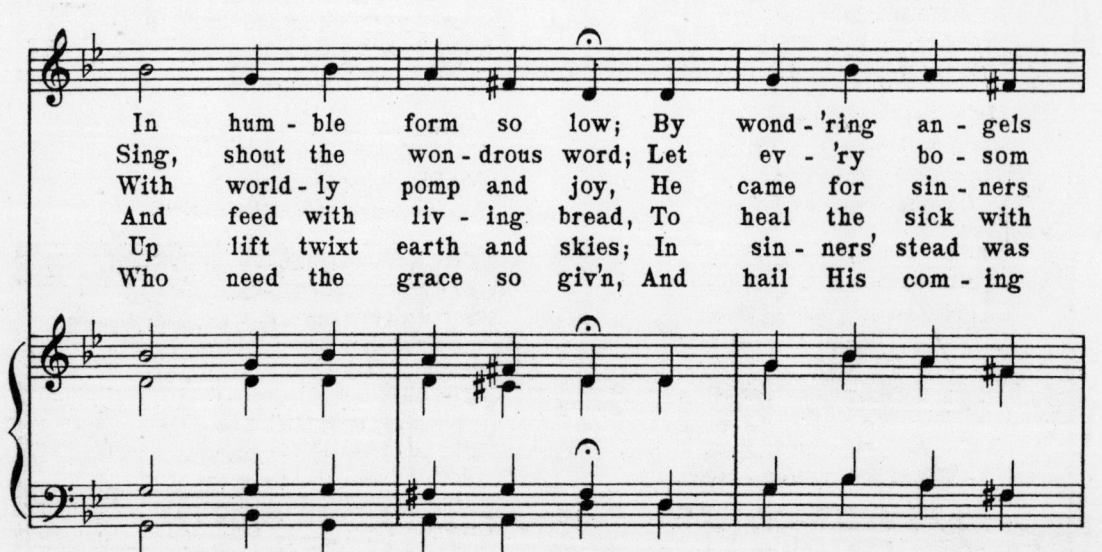

In humble form so low; By wond-'ring angels
Sing, shout the won-drous word; Let ev-'ry bosom
With world-ly pomp and joy, He came for sinners
And feed with liv-ing bread, To heal the sick with
Up lift twixt earth and skies; In sinners' stead was
Who need the grace so giv'n, And hail His coming

Silent Night
Stille Nacht

Franz Gruber

1. Silent night, Holy night! All is calm, all is bright
2. Silent night, Holy night! Shepherds quake at the sight!
3. Silent night, Holy night! Son of God, loves pure light

'Round yon Virgin Mother and Child. Holy Infant so tender and mild,
Glories stream from heaven afar, Heav'nly hosts sing Alleluia;
Radiant beams from Thy holy face, With the dawn of redeeming grace,

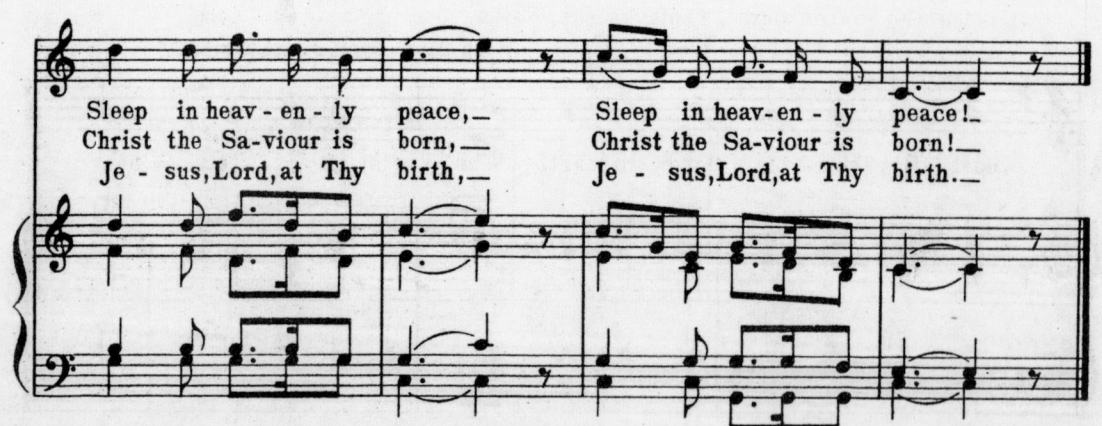

Sleep in heavenly peace,— Sleep in heavenly peace!—
Christ the Saviour is born,— Christ the Saviour is born!—
Jesus, Lord, at Thy birth,— Jesus, Lord, at Thy birth.—

W. M. Co. 4141

As Each Happy Christmas

Alle Jahre wieder

English version by Harriet R. Krauth

Johann Christian Rinck
1770–1846

1. As each hap-py Christ-mas Dawns on earth a-gain,
2. En-ters with His bless-ing In-to ev-'ry home,
3. All un-known, be-side me He will ev-er stand,

Comes the ho-ly Christ-child To the hearts of men.
Guides and guards our foot-steps, As we go and come.
And will safe-ly lead me With His own right hand.

W. M. Co. 4141

O Christmas Tree
O Tannenbaum

From the German

1. O Christmas Tree! O Christmas Tree! Thy leaves are so unchanging; Not only green when summer's here, But also when 'tis cold and drear. O Christmas Tree! O Christmas Tree! Thy leaves are so unchanging!

2. O Christmas Tree! O Christmas Tree! Much pleasure thou can'st give me; How often has the Christmas tree Afforded me the greatest glee! O Christmas Tree! O Christmas Tree! Much pleasure thou can'st give me.

3. O Christmas Tree! O Christmas Tree! Thy candles shine so brightly! From base to summit, gay and bright, There's only splendor for the sight. O Christmas Tree! O Christmas Tree! Thy candles shine so brightly!

4. O Christmas Tree! O Christmas Tree! How richly God has decked thee! Thou bidst us true and faithful be, And trust in God unchangingly. O Christmas Tree! O Christmas Tree! How richly God has decked thee.

O Come, Little Children
Ihr Kinderlein, kommet

J. P. A. Schulz

1. O come, little children, O come, one and all, O come to the manger in Bethlehem's stall; Come
2. O see in that manger the glory beams shine, A sight most inspiring, a wonder divine! An
3. O children, come hither this festival night, See Mary and Joseph, how great their delight! While
4. Come, children, come worship this heavenly Child, Reposing in slumber so sweet and so mild: Come
5. O, say to Him, Jesus, so fair and so pure, How bitter the suff'rings which Thou must endure! Here
6. We'll bring Thee glad hearts as our off'rings today; Receive them, O Jesus, and keep them alway. O

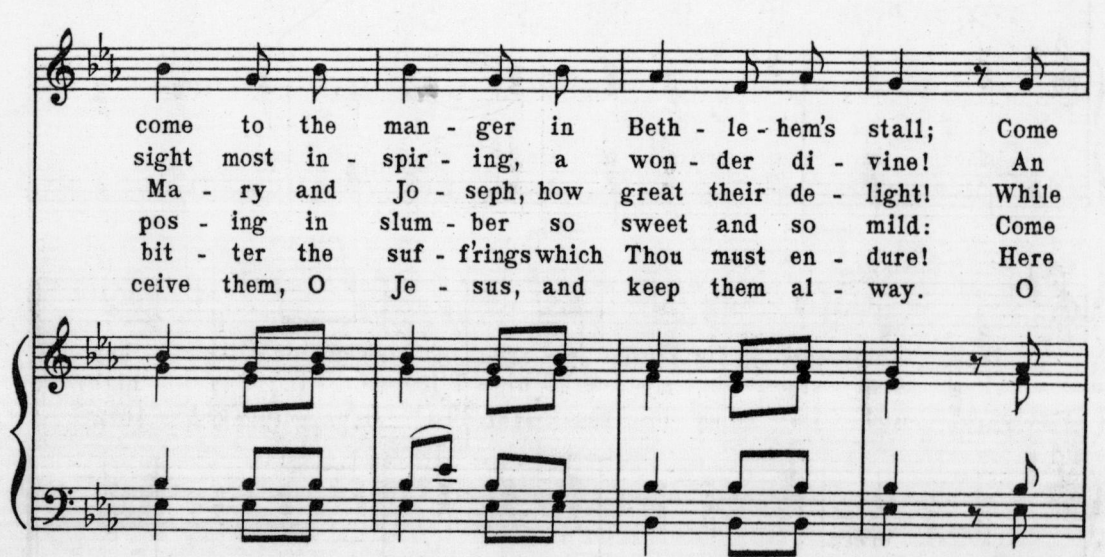

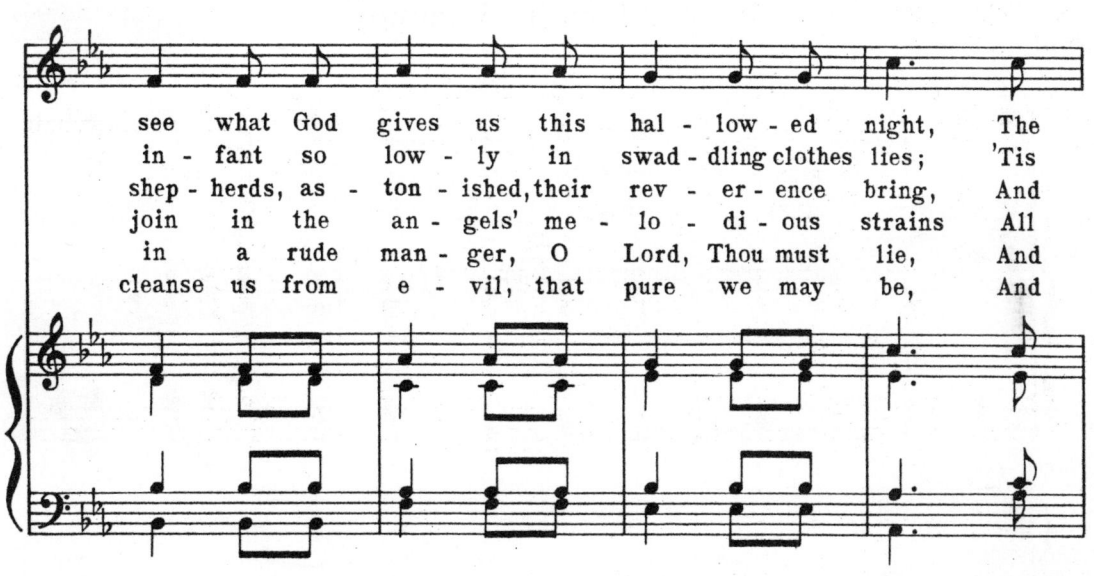

see what God gives us this hal-low-ed night, The
in-fant so low-ly in swad-dling clothes lies; 'Tis
shep-herds, as-ton-ished, their rev-er-ence bring, And
join in the an-gels' me-lo-di-ous strains All
in a rude man-ger, O Lord, Thou must lie, And
cleanse us from e-vil, that pure we may be, And

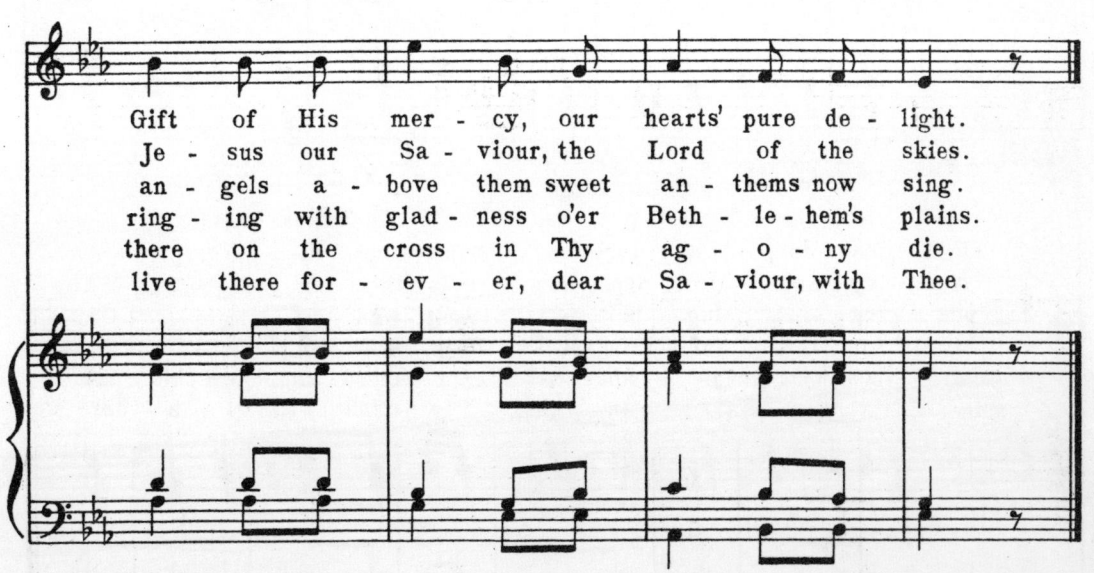

Gift of His mer-cy, our hearts' pure de-light.
Je-sus our Sa-viour, the Lord of the skies.
an-gels a-bove them sweet an-thems now sing.
ring-ing with glad-ness o'er Beth-le-hem's plains.
there on the cross in Thy ag-o-ny die.
live there for-ev-er, dear Sa-viour, with Thee.

W. M. Co. 4141

In Bethlehem, The Lowly
In Bethlehem geboren

English version
by Cecil Cowdrey

Dutch Carol
1638

1. In Bethlehem the lowly A child is born this day. Him have I chosen solely My comfort and my stay. Ah yes! Ah yes! A child is born this day.

2. My heart shall still confess thee; Thy name will I adore. In grief and gladness bless Thee If longer, yet the more. Ah yes! Ah yes! Thy name will I adore.

W. M. Co. 4141

Let our Gladness know no End

Words traditional
Old Bohemian

1. Let our gladness know no end, Hal-le-lu - jah! Un-to earth did Christ de-scend, Hal-le-lu - jah!
2. See the loveliest blooming rose, Hal-le-lu - jah! From the branch of Jes - se grows, Hal-le-lu - jah!
3. In-to flesh is made the Word, Hal-le-lu - jah! 'Tis our Re-fuge, Christ the Lord, Hal-le-lu - jah!

1-3. On this day God gave us Christ, His Son, to save us. Christ, His son, His son to save us.

W. M. Co. 4141

Come, all ye Shepherds!

English version by Cecil Cowdrey

Old Bohemian
VI Century

1. Come, all ye shep-herds, such won-ders to know. Come, where the young Child is laid, let us go! This day to us a Sa-viour is giv-en, Whom God the Lord hath sent down from heav-en, Come and fear not.
2. Hear with what won-der the tid-ings are fraught. Beth-le-hem's shep-herds great joy they have brought. Good will from heav-en, to man is giv-en, Peace nev-er end-ing to earth de-scend-ing, Glo-ry to God.
3. Haste we to Beth-le-hem, there to be-hold Him, of whose com-ing glad an-gels have told. There to His glo-ry tell we the sto-ry, Glad voi-ces rais-ing Him ev-er prais-ing, Hal-le-lu-jah!

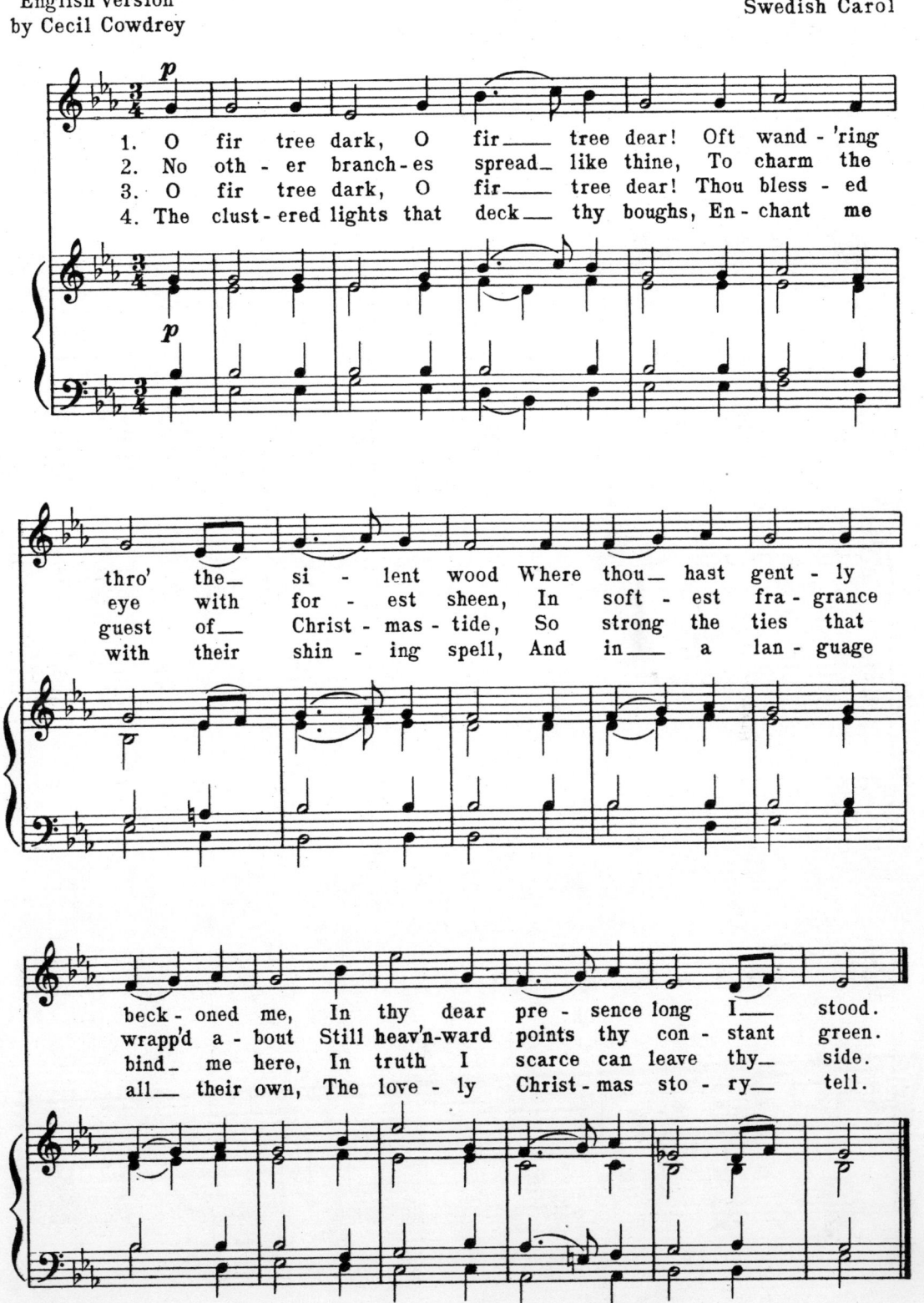

Christmas brings Joy to every Heart
Danish Carol

English version
by Cecil Cowdrey

C. E. F. Weise

1. Christ-mas brings joy to ev - 'ry heart, Sets old and young re-
2. Joy comes to all the world to-day! To hall and cot - tage
3. Once to this earth our Sa - viour came, An in - fant poor and

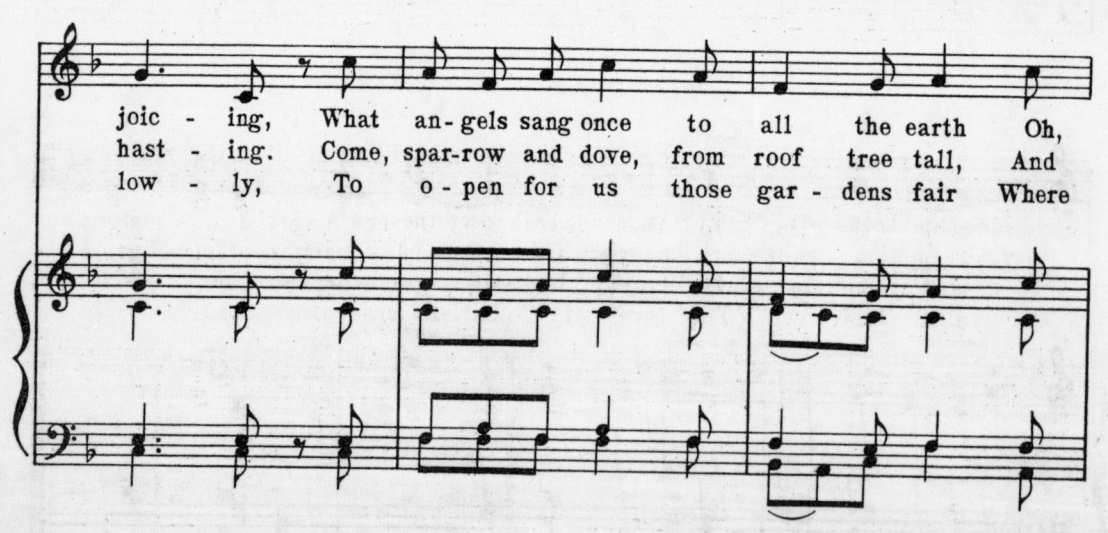

joic - ing, What an - gels sang once to all the earth Oh,
hast - ing. Come, spar-row and dove, from roof tree tall, And
low - ly, To o - pen for us those gar - dens fair Where

W. M.Co. 4141

Oh, sleep, sleep on, thou fair Child Jesus

English version
by Cecil Cowdrey

Alsatian Carol

As Lately We Watched

Austrian Carol

1. As late-ly we watch'd o'er our fields thro' the night, A star there was seen of such glo-ri-ous light; All thro' the night, an-gels did sing, In ca-rols so sweet of the birth of a King.
2. A King of such beaut-y was ne'er be-fore seen, And Ma-ry his moth-er so like to a queen. Blest be the hour, wel-come the morn, For Christ our dear Sav-iour on earth now is born.
3. His throne is a man-ger, his court is a loft, But troops of bright an-gels, in lays sweet and soft, Him they pro-claim, our Christ by name, And earth, sky and air straight are fill'd with His fame.
4. Then shep-herds, be joy-ful, sa-lute your liege King, Let hills and dales ring to the song that ye sing; Blest be the hour, wel-come the morn, For Christ our dear Sav-iour on earth now is born.

W. M. Co. 4141

In a Manger He is Lying

English version
by Cecil Cowdrey

Polish Carol

Kolyada, Kolyada*

English version by Cecil Cowdrey

Russian Carol

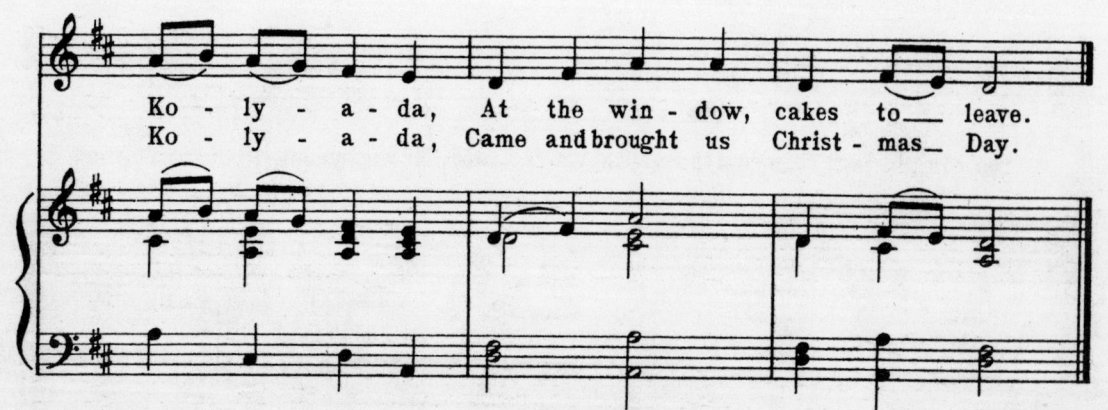

1. Ko-ly-a-da,— Ko-ly-a-da, Walks a-bout on Christ-mas eve. Ko-ly-a-da,— Ko-ly-a-da, At the win-dow, cakes to leave.
2. Ko-ly-a-da,— Ko-ly-a-da, Come this Ho-ly Night we pray. Ko-ly-a-da,— Ko-ly-a-da, Came and brought us Christ-mas Day.

* "Father Christmas," or Santa Claus.

W. M. Co. 4141

Sleep, my Little One
Slaap, mijn Kindjelief

English version by Cecil Cowdrey

Dutch Carol 1697

1. "Sleep, my lit-tle one, sleep, my dear-est one," Ma-ry sings ev - er to her child, "Sleep, my heart's de-light, Sleep, my treas-ure bright," Sings the fa-ther as low and mild.
2. Tired of play at last, close thy two eyes fast, Wind and cold thou need'st not fear, Harm shall not come to thee, Safe shall thy slum-ber be, Sleep, thy moth-er is watch-ing near.

Chorus

Sing and a-dore Him, ye lit-tle ones all; His hands and his feet, see how ten-der and small!
Sing and a-dore Him with tune-ful voice, Ye bright host of An-gels, O sing and re-joice!

W. M. Co. 4141

The Angel and the Shepherds

Translated by
Rev. S. Baring Gould

French Flanders Melody

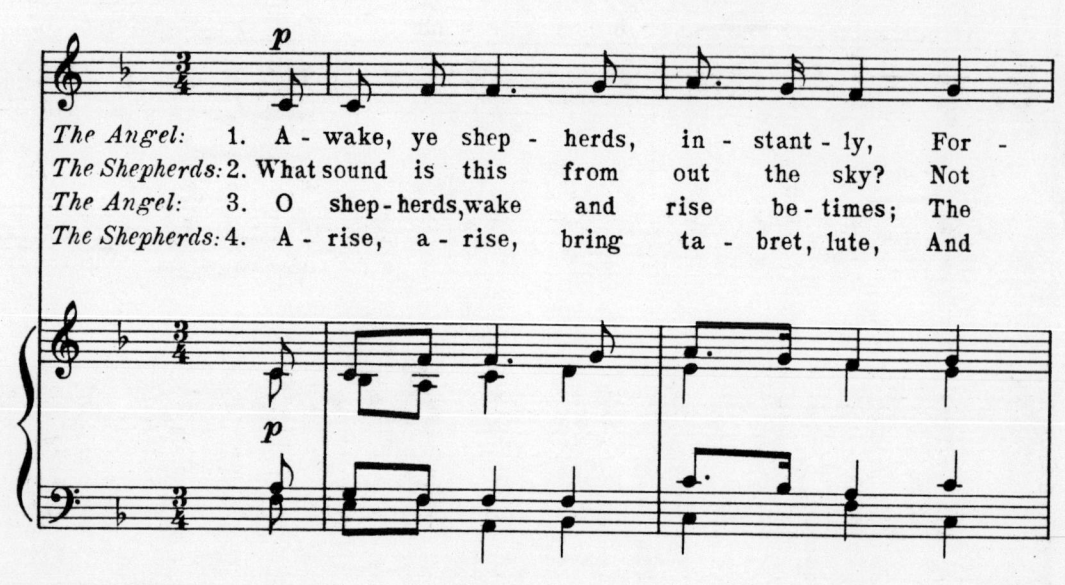

The Angel: 1. A-wake, ye shep-herds, in-stant-ly, For-
The Shepherds: 2. What sound is this from out the sky? Not
The Angel: 3. O shep-herds, wake and rise be-times; The
The Shepherds: 4. A-rise, a-rise, bring ta-bret, lute, And

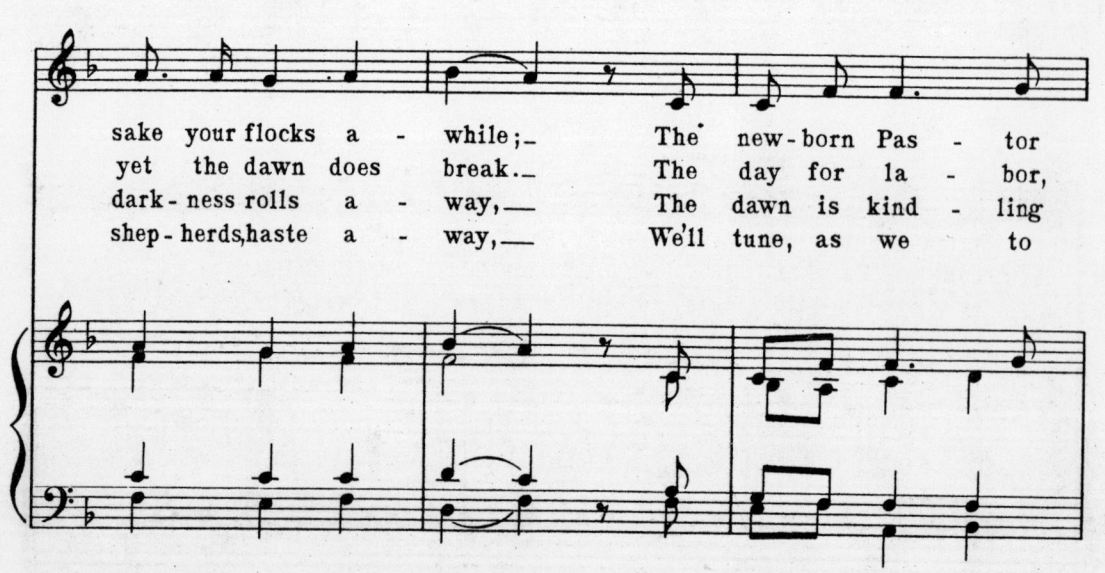

sake your flocks a - while;— The new-born Pas - tor
yet the dawn does break.— The day for la - bor,
dark-ness rolls a - way,— The dawn is kind - ling
shep-herds, haste a - way,— We'll tune, as we to

Shepherds! Shake off your Drowsy Sleep
Chantons! Bargiés, Noué, Noué

Besançon Carol

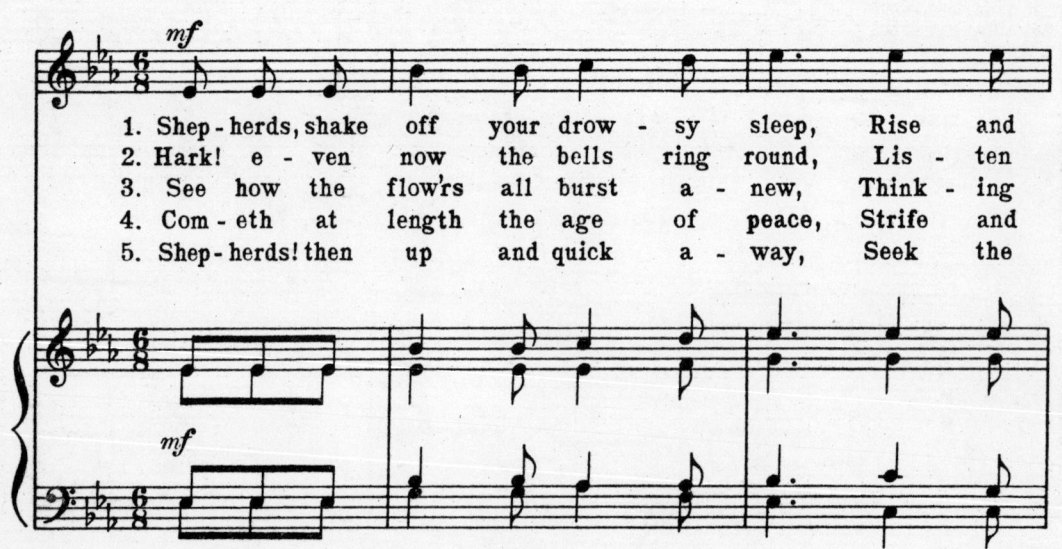

1. Shep-herds, shake off your drow-sy sleep, Rise and
2. Hark! e-ven now the bells ring round, Lis-ten
3. See how the flow'rs all burst a-new, Think-ing
4. Com-eth at length the age of peace, Strife and
5. Shep-herds! then up and quick a-way, Seek the

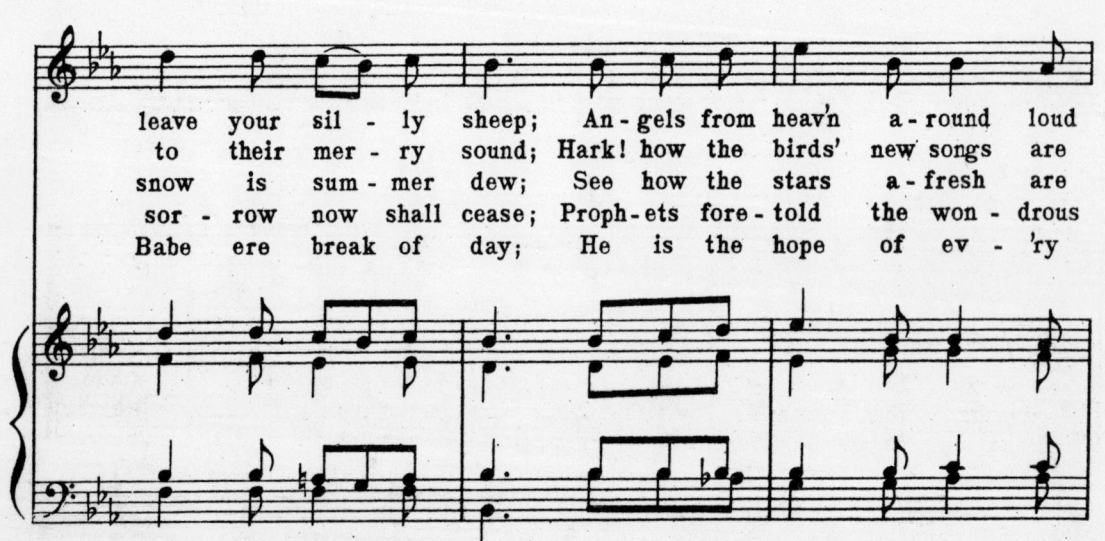

leave your sil-ly sheep; An-gels from heav'n a-round loud
to their mer-ry sound; Hark! how the birds' new songs are
snow is sum-mer dew; See how the stars a-fresh are
sor-row now shall cease; Proph-ets fore-told the won-drous
Babe ere break of day; He is the hope of ev-'ry

sing - ing, Tid - ings of great joy are bring - ing.
mak - ing, As if win - ter's chains were break - ing.
glow - ing, All their bright - est beams be - stow - ing. Shep-herds! the
sto - ry Of this Heav'n born Prince of Glo - ry.
na - tion, All in Him shall find sal - va - tion.

cho - rus come and swell! Sing No - ël, oh sing No - ël!

Angels we have Heard on High

Bergers, pour qui cette fête?

Ancient Noël

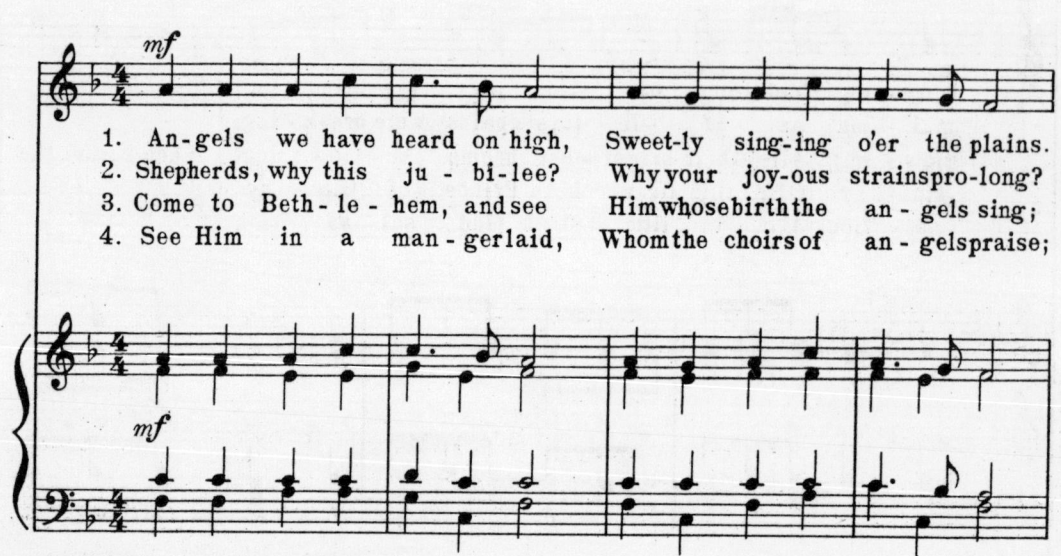

1. An-gels we have heard on high, Sweet-ly sing-ing o'er the plains.
2. Shepherds, why this ju-bi-lee? Why your joy-ous strains pro-long?
3. Come to Beth-le-hem, and see Him whose birth the an-gels sing;
4. See Him in a man-ger laid, Whom the choirs of an-gels praise;

And the moun-tains in re-ply, Ech-o-ing their joy-ous strains.
What the glad-some tid-ings be Which in-spire your heav'n-ly song?
Come, a-dore on bend-ed knee, Christ the Lord, the new-born King.
Ma-ry, Jo-seph, lend your aid, While our hearts in love we raise.

W. M. Co. 4141

Close by the Ox and the Ass so Gray
Entre le boeuf et l'âne gris

English version by Cecil Cowdrey

French Noël
1648

1. Close by the ox and the ass so gray,
2. Cradl-ed He lies 'mid the fra-grant hay,
3. Kneel-ing be-side Him the shep-herds pray.

Soft, soft, sleeps the Child to-day! An-gels watch o'er Him, Thousand ser-aph-im Hov-er bright a-bove This dear God of Love!

W.M.Co. 4141

Glad News from Bethlehem, my Comrade
Mes esta dí

English version by Cecil Cowdrey

Noël Provençal by Ranquet

1. Glad news from Bethlehem, my comrade, Tidings were brought at break of morn, How in a low and cheerless stable, God of a Virgin Mother was born. The shining angels turn to greet The dawn with sweetest lay, Ere to the Babe of Bethlehem they haste away.

2. Laid in a manger, oh, how shameful, Trembling above the chilly ground, Naked, He lieth near His mother, He for whose needs no clothes are found. Whitest of garments we will bring To clothe the Saviour fair. We, too, will haste to Bethlehem, to robe him there.

3. When has earth seen a fairer mother? When has earth seen a fairer child? Bright as the stars in heaven sparkling, Glitter their foreheads pure and mild. What shall we say, O God of love, In awe beholding them? Mother and Child we soon shall see at Bethlehem!

Ah! Great is our Good Fortune
Ai! la bono fortuno

English version by Cecil Cowdrey

Noël Provençal de Saboly, 1670

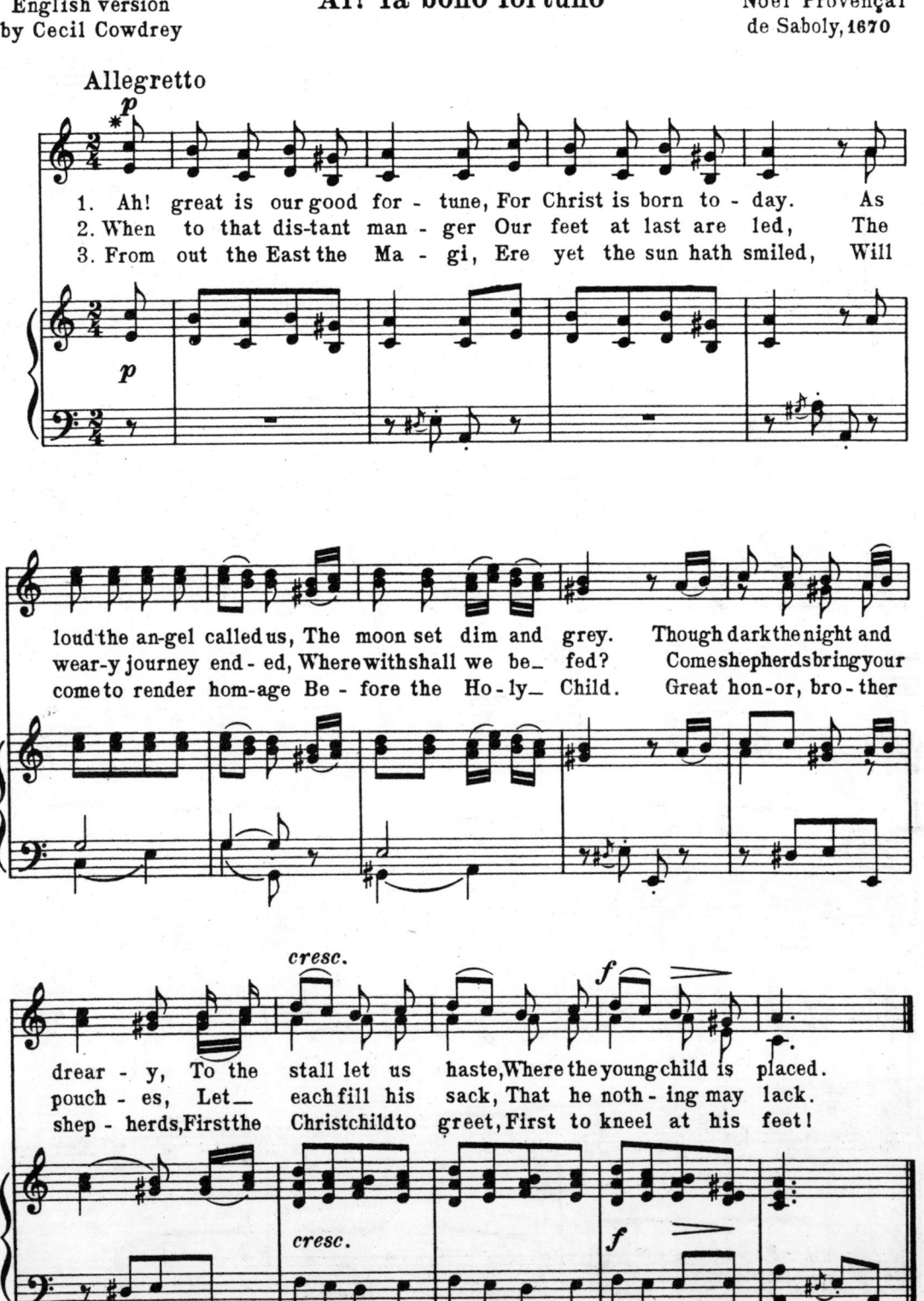

1. Ah! great is our good for-tune, For Christ is born to-day. As loud the an-gel called us, The moon set dim and grey. Though dark the night and drear-y, To the stall let us haste, Where the young child is placed.
2. When to that dis-tant man-ger Our feet at last are led, The wear-y journey end-ed, Wherewith shall we be fed? Come shepherds bring your pouch-es, Let each fill his sack, That he noth-ing may lack.
3. From out the East the Ma-gi, Ere yet the sun hath smiled, Will come to render hom-age Be-fore the Ho-ly Child. Great hon-or, bro-ther shep-herds, First the Christ child to greet, First to kneel at his feet!

* This carol may be sung either as a duet or in unison

W. M. Co. 4141

The Children at the Manger
Les enfants à la Crecho

English version
by Cecil Cowdrey

Noël Provençal
de Basquet

*This carol may be sung either as a duet or in unison

The Message of Christmas Morn
Lei pastorieu

English version by Julius Mattfeld

Noël Provençal de Saboly, 1670

1. The shepherds they had gathered on the hillside, A shepherd throng that met in solemn
2. To Bethlehem, great David's royal city, Thence straightway would they go without de-
3. A myriad stars bedeck the sombre heavens Above the place where Jesus Christ is
4. This day a child to Mary born and Joseph, Emmanuel, God with us, we shall

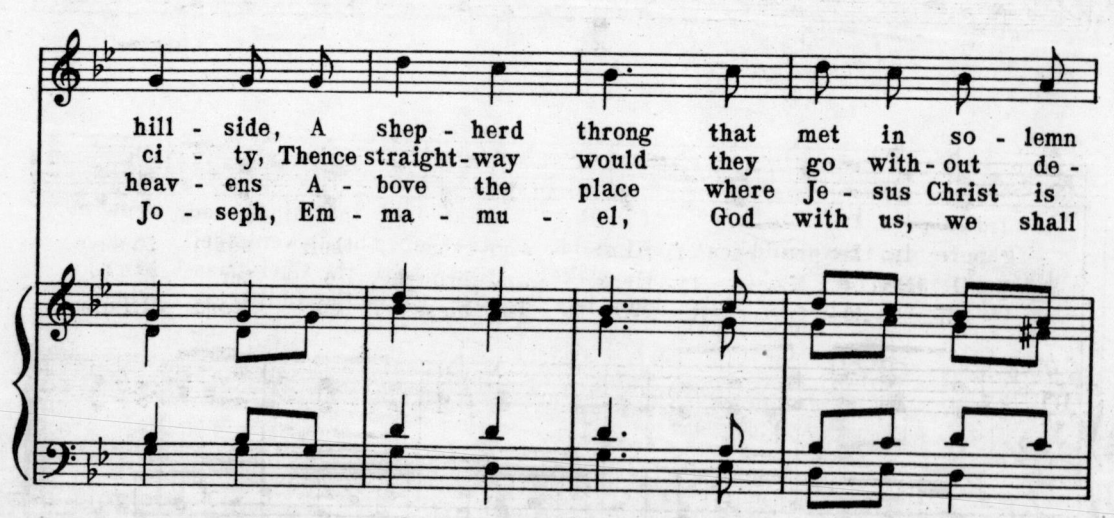

W. M. Co. 4141

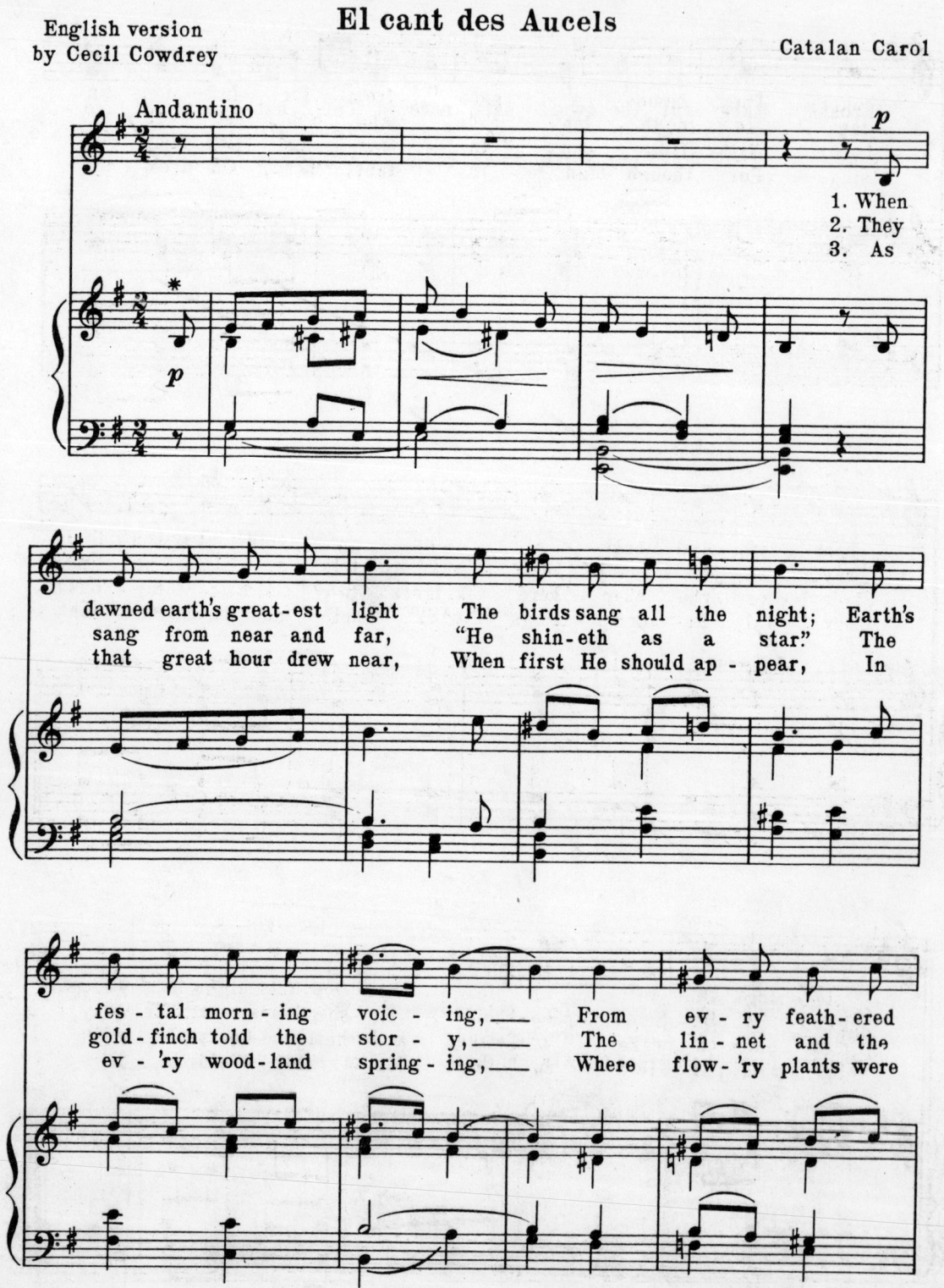

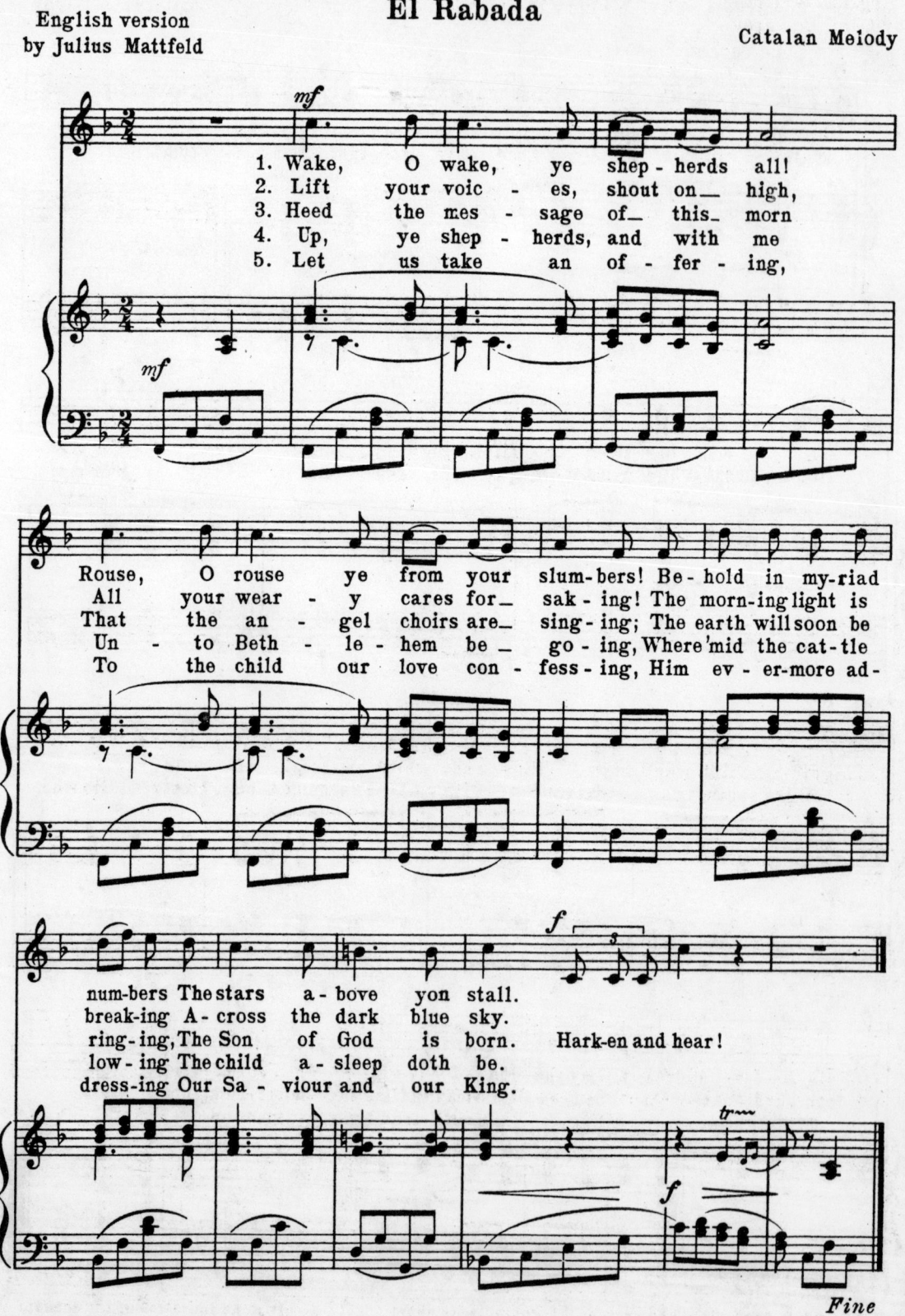

Come All Ye Children
Venid, niños queridos

English version by Cecil Cowdrey

Castillan Melody

Andantino

Come, all ye chil-dren, your gen-tle voic-es u-nite, Wel-come this hour with your glad-est ca-rols to-night. O re-joice! Sing ye, well pleased that your ac-cents of love, Sweet-ly as-cend to the Christ-child a-bove, Sing, for His birth Bringeth peace to men up-on earth!

* This carol may be sung either as a duet or in unison.

W. M. Co. 4141

All that Wondrous Christmas Night
Noite de Natal

English version by Cecil Cowdrey

Portuguese Carol

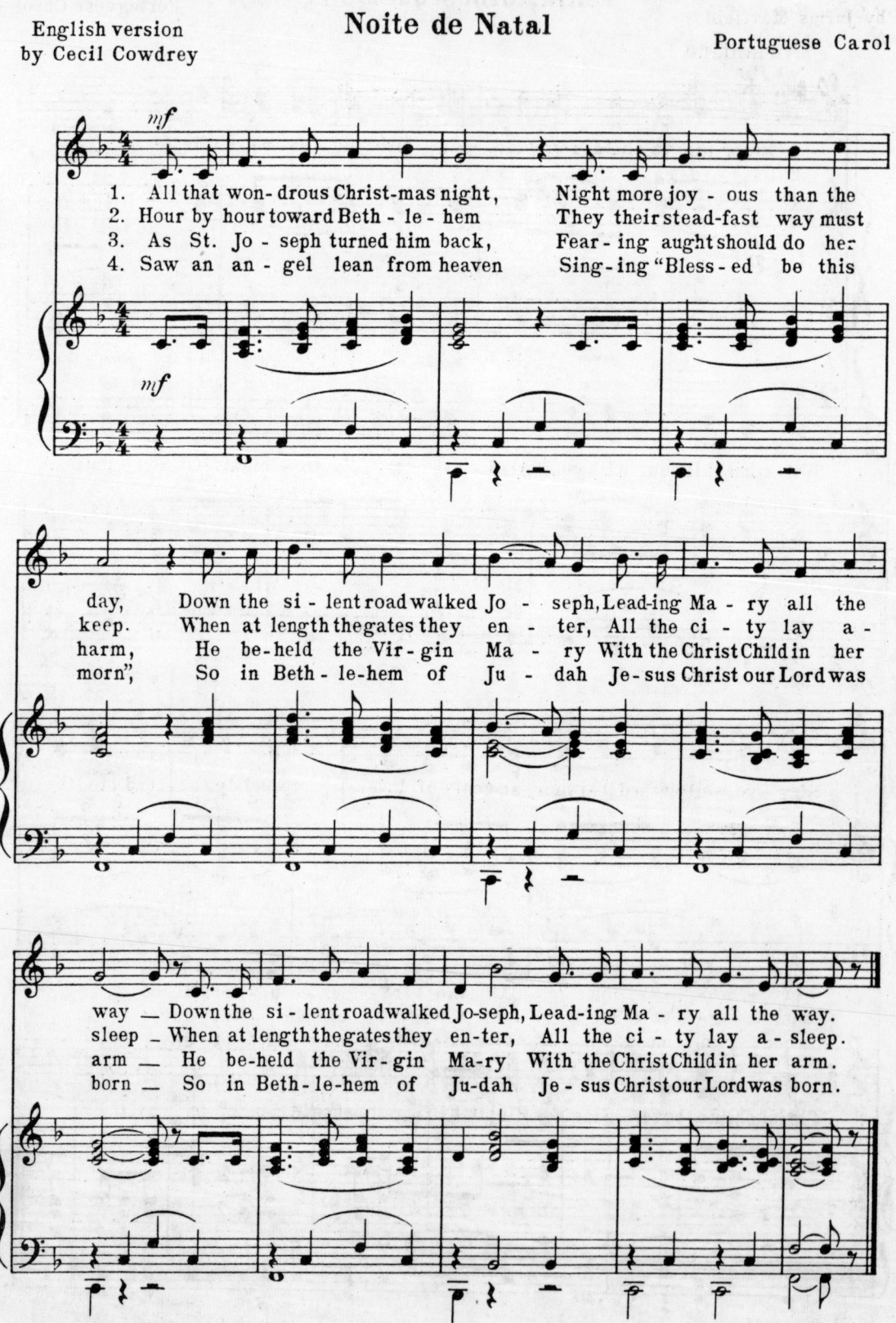

1. All that wondrous Christmas night, Night more joyous than the day, Down the silent road walked Joseph, Leading Mary all the way — Down the silent road walked Joseph, Leading Mary all the way.
2. Hour by hour toward Bethlehem They their steadfast way must keep. When at length the gates they enter, All the city lay asleep — When at length the gates they enter, All the city lay asleep.
3. As St. Joseph turned him back, Fearing aught should do her harm, He beheld the Virgin Mary With the Christ Child in her arm — He beheld the Virgin Mary With the Christ Child in her arm.
4. Saw an angel lean from heaven Singing "Blessed be this morn", So in Bethlehem of Judah Jesus Christ our Lord was born — So in Bethlehem of Judah Jesus Christ our Lord was born.

W. M. Co. 4141

From the Orient they came a-Riding
Os Reis

English version by Julius Mattfeld

Portuguese Carol

1. From the O - ri - ent they came a - rid - ing, ___ Three good kings of hum-ble heart and mien, To be-hold the Lord of Heav-en, Come to earth a child to be.
2. Guid - ed east - ward by a star they journ - eyed, ___ And to Beth - le - hem they came at last, Where the In - fant Lord was sleep-ing On the Vir - gin Moth - er's knee.
3. Pre-cious gifts of gold and myrrh and in - cense, ___ Bring-ing God the gifts by God de-signed, Low the Kings in hom - age bow - ing At the feet of Ma - ry lay.
4. Not a word or whis-per do they ut - ter, ___ Lest the Child from saint-ly sleep a-wake, But in ad - o - ra - tion meek-ly Wor-ship till the break of day.

W. M. Co. 4141

When Christ was Born on Earth
Song of the Bagpipers

English version by Cecil Cowdrey

Neapolitan Carol

1. When Christ was born on earth On that most bless-ed night, Like noon-day shone the stars All beau-ti-ful, all bright. Toward earth in-
2. In all the peace-ful land No en-e-my was found; The li-on wan-dered free, The tim-id sheep a-round; Young lambs were
3. Where shep-herds watched their flocks, There came an an-gel bright, More ra-diant than the sun, He shone with heaven-ly light. All fear al-

* This carol may be sung either as a duet or in unison.

W. M. Co. 4141

Lully, Lully, Lu

English version
by Cecil Cowdrey

Latin Carol
15th Century

1. He who heav'n cre - a - ted, Lul-ly, lul-ly, lu!
In a low-ly stall doth lie, Bye, bye, bye, bye, bye.
He who reigns in heav'n most high, Lul-ly, lul-ly, lu!

2. Jo-seph brought the swaddling clothes, Bye, bye, bye, bye, bye.
Swathed by Ma-ry, Moth-er mild, Lul-ly, lul-ly, lu.
In the man-ger lay the child, Bye, bye, bye, bye, bye.

3. Close be-side the cat-tle there, Lul-ly, lul-ly, lu!
Slept the Joy of all the earth, Bye, bye, bye, bye, bye.
Love-li-ness be-yond com-pare, Lul-ly, lul-ly, lu!

W. M. Co. 4141

O Come, All Ye Faithful
Adeste Fideles

English version
by Rev. F. Oakeley, 1841

J. Reading, 1692

1. O come, all ye faithful, joyful and triumphant; Oh come ye, Oh come ye to Bethlehem;
2. God of God, Light of Light Lo! He abhors not the Virgin's womb;
3. Sing, choirs of angels, sing in exultation, Sing, all ye citizens of heav'n above:
4. Yea, Lord, we greet Thee, born this happy morning; Jesus, to Thee be glory giv'n;

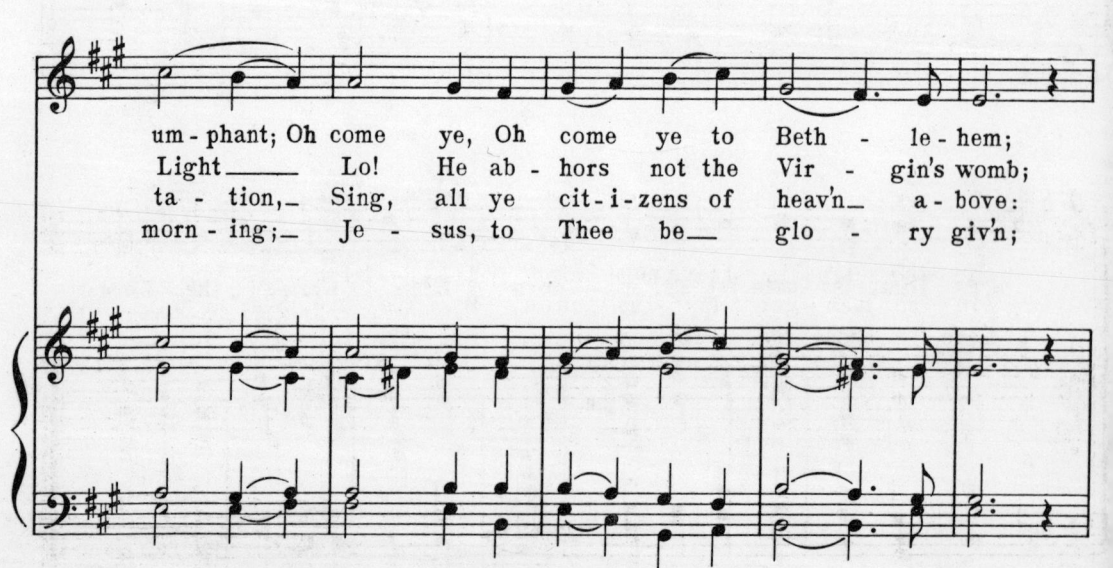

OPERETTAS
FOR GRADE SCHOOL STUDENTS

THE THANKSGIVING STORY BOOK
By **Lois Wilson** and **Mary F. Lehnard**

An operetta in three episodes. Time of performance, one hour.

A story of 1630 prepared especially for the Thanksgiving holiday.

Vocal Score, Piano Acc. **60 cents**

AT THE END OF THE WARPATH
By **John Iroquois**

Operetta in a prologue and three acts. Unison and two-part. Time of performance, one hour.

An Indian legend telling the story of two brothers lost in a forest at different times, who are finally found and recognized by their father.

Vocal Score, Piano Acc. **60 cents**

DAME DURDEN'S SCHOOL
By **May H. Brahe**

An operetta in one act, one scene. Time of performance, one hour. A story of the fairies who try to correct the habits of lazy children. Sung in unison throughout.

Vocal Score, Piano Acc. **60 cents**

WASHINGTON'S BIRTHDAY
By **Lina Loring**

A juvenile operetta in two acts to be sung in unison or two-parts. A story of George Washington's youth. Can be given by boys, girls, or both.

Vocal Score, Piano Acc., Dialogue and Directions for Stage Business, etc. **60 cents**

AUNT DRUSILLA'S GARDEN
By **John S. Fearis**

An operetta in two acts sung in unison. Time of performance, one hour and a half.

The story of a poor girl who after many trials wins happiness and wealth.

Vocal Score, Piano Acc. **$1.00**

Stage Manager's Guide **$1.00**
Orchestral Parts Available on Rental

THE MAGIC WOOD
By **May H. Brahe**

A humorous operetta in one act for treble voices. Time of performance about fifty minutes.

The story of mischievous boys who are punished by the fairies for molesting a group of girls enjoying a picnic.

Vocal Score, Piano Acc. **60 cents**

THE WILLIS MUSIC CO.   Cincinnati, Ohio